Rescue Rosie's
Canal Adventures

Rescue Rosie's Canal Adventures

Andrew Chapman
Illustrated by Sarah Hoggard

Matador
9 Priory Business Park,
Wistow Road, Kibworth Beauchamp,
Leicestershire. LE8 0RX
Tel: 0116 279 2299
Email: books@troubador.co.uk
Web: www.troubador.co.uk/matador
Twitter: @matadorbooks

ISBN 978 1788039 512

British Library Cataloguing in Publication Data.
A catalogue record for this book is available from the British Library.

Printed and bound by CPI Group (UK) Ltd, Croydon, CR0 4YY
Typeset in 11pt Book Antiqua by Troubador Publishing Ltd, Leicester, UK

Matador is an imprint of Troubador Publishing Ltd

To my Wife, Kath, with thanks for all her support and encouragement.

Preface

Where is Rosie? Look out for the clues in each adventure and check your answer at the end of each story.

Chapter 1

Go for it Rosie!

Rosie is a big blue canal boat and is home to Skipper Pete and his fluffy, scruffy dog, Henry. She is very long but very narrow. When Skipper Pete goes to bed at night his head touches one side of Rosie and his feet the other.

Rosie is around forty years old and for all this time she and Skipper Pete have been great friends. They spend their days travelling the English canals and rivers and at night they love to talk about their adventures and remember all the fun they have had. When it comes to cruising Rosie knows what to do but needs Skipper Pete's help when she gets to locks. A lock is a way of climbing a hill in a boat and is quite complicated to work, but Rosie and Skipper Pete have been working together as a team for so long that everything usually goes smoothly.

It was a sunny morning in early autumn. Rosie, Skipper Pete and Henry had spent the night near some

locks on a canal in Lancashire. Because of the time of year the grass on the canal bank was wet with dew and Henry loved nothing better than to run around in the damp grass and roll on his back. When Skipper Pete called him he raced back to Rosie, ran through the door and then jumped on Pete's favourite chair. Pete knew that this meant he wouldn't be able to sit down until Henry and the chair had dried off so he said:

"Better get going Rosie old girl. We have twenty three locks to do today and the sooner we start the better."

"OK Skipper Pete, I'm ready," she said and started her engine with a little puff of smoke.

Pete had been in the navy for many years and loved being on the water. He still felt a sense of excitement at the beginning of a new day, as you never really know if it will be the start of some great adventure.

When there are a lot of locks together it is known as a flight, like stairs because that is exactly what they are, a set of stairs all filled with water. Today Rosie was climbing the first two locks before a short flat stretch and then the main flight of twenty one,

2

which would take her up about seventy metres. Pete opened the lock gates and Rosie cruised gently in. Pete closed the gates, filled the lock and opened the top gates and Rosie was through the first one. Only twenty two to go! The next lock had brand new gates and looked very smart. Lock gates are made of wood, usually oak, and are very heavy. It takes a team of workmen and a crane to fit new gates but if they do a good job the new gates will be completely watertight. Rosie was really glad about this because when lock gates leak her face can get very wet indeed and Pete was glad because leaking gates are more difficult to open.

They were soon half way up the main flight and Rosie and Skipper Pete were working well as a team. As it was a Sunday there were plenty of people about: walkers, joggers, fishermen and people who just loved to watch boats pass through the locks. Henry was now dry and had decided to run around the sides of the locks and amuse everyone by chasing his tail, growling when he couldn't catch it and then

falling over when he got too dizzy. People would stop to talk to Rosie and Pete and one of the most common questions was, "How long would it take to climb the flight of locks?" Skipper Pete was always a bit embarrassed by this question because it would take him and Rosie over five hours to get through the locks and travel the two miles. People usually laughed when he told them but Pete sometimes thought they were envious of such a slow and relaxed way of life.

Rosie was five locks from the top and looking forward to stopping for a while. It was a warm day now and Skipper Pete was getting hot and red in the face. Rosie had seen him like this before and knew that although he was kind and gentle he could get a bit cross if she did anything wrong. Pete opened the top gates and Rosie tried to move out of the lock but nothing happened. Her engine was running but she couldn't move forward. She tried to reverse but still nothing happened.

"Skipper Pete," she said a bit timidly.

"Yes Rosie," Pete replied.

"I can't move."

"How's that? Not at all?"

"No, I don't know what's wrong." Rosie was so pleased that Pete hadn't got annoyed.

"I'd better take a look then," he said. Pete got into the engine room to find what could be wrong. Eventually he climbed out, scratching his head. He had found out what the problem was. Rosie's propeller was missing. It must have been loose and dropped off when she entered this lock. He explained this and said that the only thing to do was to get to a boatyard where a mechanic could fit a new one. The big problem was that she would have to be taken out of the water with a huge crane. This had happened to Rosie before and she didn't like it. She preferred being a boat to an aeroplane!

"The only problem, Rosie," said Pete now that he had a plan, "is that the nearest boatyard is ten miles away. How will we get there?"

"We could ask that boat moored at the side of the canal for a tow."

Pete thought this was an excellent idea and went to speak to the crew. The boat was very smart with beautiful glossy red paintwork. He was considerably younger than Rosie and the colours of his decoration and polished brass made Rosie feel rather scruffy. "I do hope he is friendly and can help us," she thought. She needn't have worried. As the smart red boat reversed into the lock next to her he said,

"Good afternoon, my name is Sadiq, I do hope I can be of assistance." Rosie found him very easy to talk to and before long they were chatting as if they had known each other for years. His crew helped Skipper Pete tie the two boats side by side and then they glided out of the lock together. This seemed very strange to Rosie as she was now moving without her engine as Sadiq skilfully manoeuvred them both into the next lock. Rosie felt completely at ease as she heard Pete and Sadiq's crew talking and laughing together. An hour later they had reached

5

the top of the climb and moored up so that the crews could have lunch and a bit of a rest. Pete was invited onto Sadiq to share the crew's lunch and this made Rosie feel a little jealous. She may have broken down but she could still put on a good lunch! She didn't feel upset for too long as Skipper Pete came out to talk to her. He explained that Sadiq would now tow her to the boatyard, as it would be a lot quicker than going side by side. Rosie had never been towed before and wasn't sure what to expect. Sadiq's crew used such a short rope that the only thing that Rosie could see was his back and that made her go cross-eyed so that she started seeing double.

After three hours Sadiq and Rosie arrived at the boatyard. Although Rosie had not been able to see very much she had been able to hear Sadiq talking to passers by on the towpath. Everyone was interested to know what had happened, as they did not see boats being towed these days. Many years ago when canals had been the main way of transporting goods it had been a common sight to see boats travelling in pairs, each one carrying as much cargo as a full size truck. Sadiq had been very modest, telling people that he was just helping out and doing what any boat would have done. Rosie was very impressed by Sadiq and people's reaction to what he was doing. She had not been able to see any of the people or birds and animals she would normally talk to so she was quite glad when the journey was over and she was moored at the wharf. She and Sadiq talked a bit more before he headed off on his own adventures.

He told her how much he had enjoyed helping her and Skipper Pete. It had made him feel really good and he had been happy to help. Rosie thanked him from the bottom of her fuel tank.

Once Sadiq and his crew had gone and it was just Skipper Pete, Rosie and Henry again it became peaceful once more and Rosie started thinking about and reliving today's adventure. Pete fed Henry who had woken up long enough to eat his tea and then gone back to sleep, and then started preparing his own tea. After he had eaten his meal and washed up the pots and pans he settled down in his favourite chair and with Henry dozing in his basket was soon asleep himself.

As Pete slept Rosie came to a big decision. She had been really impressed by what Sadiq had said just before he left and had decided to spend the rest of her life helping people, animals and boats and anyone else who might need her. She was going to become RESCUE ROSIE, the happiest, most helpful, most loved and respected boat on the canals and rivers of England. All she needed to do now was to convince Skipper Pete as she couldn't do it without his help. She nudged the side of the wharf so that the jolt woke Pete up. She couldn't wait to tell him of her decision and get his agreement. Although he didn't like being woken up he was very enthusiastic about the idea and said "Go for it Rosie".

Later that week a big crane came to the side of the canal and lifted Rosie out of the water. The mechanic fitted a shiny new propeller and the crane lifted her back into the water. She was so excited about her new life that she forgot to be nervous when the crane picked her up. She couldn't wait for the first adventure of RESCUE ROSIE to start.

Puzzle answer:
Wigan, Leeds and Liverpool Canal

Chapter 2

Rescue Rosie Goes into the Dark

A fine sunny morning in June, just after midsummer's day, found Rescue Rosie waking up with a bit of a start. Another canal boat had gone past too fast and the wash had bumped her against the stone wharf where she had spent the night. She, Skipper Pete and Henry were moored at a small town in Yorkshire and due to the time of year the moorings were full. The speeding craft had woken all the other moored boats and they all grumbled to each other.

"Why do people have to be in such a hurry?" moaned a cruiser in front of Rosie.

"If they want to go that fast they should use a motorbike!" groaned a narrowboat at her rear. Rosie agreed with the sentiment but secretly was quite happy to be awake on such a beautiful morning.

A family of swans glided past, the father leading five cygnets and their mother last, all in a straight line. The cygnets were growing well now and loved to flap their little stumpy wings as they imitated their parents. Rosie loved the baby birds and animals that lived by the canal at this time of year but was wary of the parents. She had never been attacked by a fully grown swan as she was considerably bigger than they were but she had seen how aggressive they could be. The cygnets and the ducklings, on the other hand, were playful and would tickle her hull by nibbling at the weed that grew on her along the waterline.

Skipper Pete was also woken up by the passing boat and was soon washed and dressed. Henry was running up and down the floor inside Rosie, eager to play and get outside into the sun. After a run along the towpath to greet all the other dogs who were living on boats, he was back for his breakfast. No sooner had Pete filled the bowl and put it on the floor, than it was empty again. "That dog!" exclaimed Pete as he shook his head and laughed to himself. "If there was a prize for speed eating at Crufts, I would enter him."

After he had eaten his breakfast, Pete sat on the deck with a second mug of coffee and thought about an engraving he had seen on a lock gate they had passed yesterday. It read:

"Super high way, super slow way, super wet way, super low way." He liked that and had written it down in his notebook.

It was now time to think about today's boating.

He and Rosie had talked it through last night and decided to climb up to the summit of this canal. It wasn't very far in a straight line but this canal was far from direct as it followed the contours of the land. This was Yorkshire moorland so the hillsides were far from smooth. They had a few locks to climb and a tunnel to pass through before they arrived at their mooring for the evening.

Rosie had already started her engine when Pete started untying her mooring ropes. They were soon out of the town and in open country. At the bottom lock of the next flight was a stone cottage that Skipper Pete had always admired. When the canals had been used for carrying goods and produce it would have been a lock keeper's house but now it was a peaceful home for a young family. It had a wonderful, traditional cottage garden and a marvellous vegetable patch. The front door of the house was surrounded by honeysuckle and was usually open so the children could run in and out. On this day the children were sitting on the wall watching the boats go past while their mother was working in the garden. Rosie moored up by the cottage, Pete went to talk to the skilled gardener and Henry went to play with the children. Henry's favourite toy was a bit of rope with a knot at each end so he took this with him in the hope that they would throw it for him. It was his lucky day!

Pete was in luck as well as he came away from the garden with some lettuce, radishes and a bag of very early potatoes.

"That's my lunch taken care of," he thought.

Once they were through this flight of locks they were out in wild country with mainly sheep for company. The spring lambs had grown considerably but were still smaller than their mothers or lambs who grazed in the valleys. They no longer frolicked but ate steadily like grown up sheep.

Up through three more locks and they were on the summit, the highest part of the canal. There were two more miles to go before they would come to the tunnel and even though they were now higher than before the countryside was less wild and there were cattle in the fields as well as sheep. The cows were mainly the black and white Friesians that are so much part of the British rural scene. It is thought that this type of cow originates from Friesland in northern Holland and was brought over to Britain around two hundred years ago.

There were more houses near the canal now and flocks of Canada geese with goslings. In one field Skipper Pete counted twenty five goslings and several adults. It looked like a school class where the subject was grass eating!

As Rosie approached the mouth of the tunnel she could see that the traffic lights were on green so it was safe for her to enter. You don't often find traffic lights on canals but when tunnels are long or too narrow to allow boats to pass lights are installed. This tunnel takes about thirty minutes to go through so if the lights are on red you can sometimes wait for a long time for them to change. Pete and Henry went inside the cabin to keep dry and Rosie switched her headlight on before entering the tunnel. She did not mind going through tunnels although they were cold and dark. She could see a small dot of daylight at the far end almost a mile away. What she did not like is the streams of cold water that sometimes poured from the roof. She could see them coming with her headlight and just had to brace herself for the cold shower.

She had been slowly and carefully moving forward through the tunnel for about ten minutes when she thought she saw something moving in the dark water. She looked more closely and there it was, a black and white cow, swimming towards her.

"Am I glad to see you," said the cow. "This water is very cold and I'm getting very bored with swimming. Turn that light out will you, you're dazzling me."

Rosie was so surprised that she didn't know what to say. Then she remembered that she was Rescue Rosie and that this was an opportunity to live up to her name. She realised that despite the cow's abrupt manner it was very cold and nearly exhausted. If she didn't act swiftly the cow could die. Without delay Rosie dropped her front rope into the water and told the cow to bite on it. She switched off her headlight and then started reversing back through the tunnel towing the cow. Skipper Pete didn't know what was going on as, despite his name, he normally let Rosie do her own thing. He was a very "chilled" skipper. Rosie told him what she was doing and as soon as he understood he went on to the back deck to shine a lamp and show other boats that they were reversing.

Due to a cow's diet they are full of gas and therefore fairly buoyant. As Rosie emerged from the tunnel mouth with the cow in tow some of the passers by thought she had been chased out of the tunnel by the angry cow while others thought she was towing a bad tempered black and white iceberg.

Rosie carried on reversing until she came to an area where a field came down to the water's edge and the cow was able to stand up. Very gingerly, the cow let go of the rope and climbed out of the canal and sat in the sunshine. She was very tired and looked very shaky. From Pete's navy days he new that a tot of rum would help revive the poor creature. He diluted a large dose of the amber liquid in canal water and poured it down the cow's throat. After five minutes it was looking a lot better and ready to explain what had happened.

"My name is Hendrika which is, of course, a Dutch name", she said with the air of someone delivering a lecture. "The farmer moved me from this field to one on the other side of the tunnel a few days ago. I didn't like it. It's colder and the wind blows straight through you. I thought to myself 'Hendrika, you are not going to put up with this. You should go back to where you were happy. The canal will be the quickest route. If a boat can go through the tunnel then so can I.' So I jumped in and started swimming. The water outside the tunnel wasn't too cold but when I was inside it was

freezing". Hendrika's voice softened a bit as she started to relive the horrible experience. "By the time you found me I was beginning to struggle and if it hadn't been for your swift action I don't think I would have made it. Thank you very much. What is your name by the way?"

"Rosie," said our heroine. "Rescue Rosie".

"Well Rosie, I think I owe you my life". With that Hendrika's brusque attitude vanished and she started talking warmly to Rosie about her life and they were soon swapping stories like old friends.

Pete took Henry to try to find the farmer who owned Hendrika. He knew that although the rum had helped revive the exhausted cow it was not the best medicine and that it would be better if a vet checked her out. He found the farmer leaning on a five bar gate watching a pair of swallows who had built a nest in an old barn and were now gathering insects to feed their young. Pete told the farmer what had happened.

The farmer chuckled and said, "You sometimes get cows like that – stroppy, I call them. That Hendrika is the worst of the lot. I have learned my lesson. I'll not shift her again. We might not be lucky enough to have you passing the next time and if anything happened to her I'd not forgive myself. I'll get the vet to check her over tomorrow morning. I thank you, Skipper Pete, for saving her and I'll come down to the canal and thank Rosie in person. She must be quite a boat!"

Pete and the farmer chatted as they walked

back to the canal while Henry ran ahead to see how Hendrika was doing. He needn't have worried. She was sitting on the canal bank deep in conversation with Rosie. When the men arrived the farmer thanked Rosie for what she had done and wished them a safe onward voyage.

Rosie went into the tunnel again feeling pleased with herself. She had done a good thing.

When they moored up for the night Pete and Henry had their tea on the deck as it was still a lovely warm evening. Pete then went inside and settled himself in his favourite chair with Henry in his basket and started telling Rosie what the farmer had said to him. Years ago another cow had fallen in the canal, chosen to swim through the tunnel and was then revived with alcohol. So history can repeat itself or was it an ancestor of Hendrika's?

Puzzle answer:
Gargrave – Foulridge, Leeds and Liverpool Canal

Chapter 3

Rescue Rosie Helps Out

I t was a sunny morning in early spring and Rescue Rosie, Skipper Pete and Henry were on a canal in Staffordshire. It had rained really heavily the night before but now the clouds had cleared and the warmth of the sunshine was making the wet countryside steam. It was really magical. Rosie had seen this many times before but it never lost its wonder.

Also living on Rosie, as well as Pete and Henry, were a family of spiders. They had been there for many years and Rosie thought that the current family must be at least the great, great, great grand children of the originals. Spiders love to build webs to catch their food and sometimes they built these over Rosie's eyes. When it rains hard the water droplets stick in the web and on this particular morning Rosie was having trouble seeing.

They were cruising along a narrow canal. It is

called this because the locks are only wide enough for one boat. When the canals were built, many years ago, they often split a farmer's fields in half. The builders put in many bridges so that the farmers were still able to get to all their land. On this canal most of the bridges were made of brick and very narrow so Rosie had to concentrate very hard to get through without touching the sides. The wet webs were making this very difficult and at every bridge she was hitting the brickwork. "Clunk, scraaaape, griiind", she went. Every time she did this it would wake Henry up and make his water slop out of his bowl. He would raise his eyes to the roof and mutter, "Oh really Rosie, can't you be more careful".

"Now then Rosie, what is going on? This is most unlike you," said Skipper Pete with a big smile on his face. He knew that Rosie was very proud of her ability and would not be hitting things unless something was wrong.

"Oh Skipper Pete," she said. "You have to help me. I can't see because the spiders have built webs over my eyes. Can you clear them off please?"

Pete now understood what was wrong and went to Rosie's front with a rag and cleaned her eyes. Once that was done she found everything a lot easier and started cruising smoothly once more. If only all problems had such simple solutions!

Rosie could feel that her diesel tank was getting empty so she warned Skipper Pete that they would need to find some more fuel soon. On the canals and rivers you can buy fuel at boatyards and also from travelling fuel boats. Rosie and Pete had not been on this canal for a long time but had heard from other boats that there was a fuel boat in this area. Just as Rosie came round a sharp bend there he was. His name was Fred and he and his skipper, Stefan, were just going through a narrow bridge themselves. Fred was an ex working boat and was almost 100 years old. His cabin was decorated with the traditional designs of roses and castles. Fred had worked in the heyday of the canals carrying goods from London to Birmingham and beyond.

When people started using lorries to transport things, seventy or more years ago, Fred was abandoned with a lot of his other old friends. Luckily they were all rescued and now enjoyed life on the canals again. They didn't have to work nearly as hard as before so they were all happy as they looked smart in new paintwork and loved the attention they got wherever they went. Today Fred was carrying diesel for boats, gas for the crews to cook with and coal to keep their stoves alight. He always went slowly as the canals are usually shallow and he didn't like scraping his bottom on the canal bed.

Rosie had to put her engine in reverse to stop herself from colliding with Fred and they then moored up side by side.

"It's just as well we found you," Rosie said to Fred. "My fuel tank was getting very empty".

"I come round this way every month," replied Fred. "I have made lots of friends round here but it's always nice to meet someone new." Fred went on to tell Rosie about his working life. Rosie could tell that he had told these stories before and with the comforting glug glug of fuel going in to her tank she was soon struggling to keep her eyes open. Skipper Pete and Stefan also chatted as Rosie's tank was filled and Henry ran around on the towpath. When Pete had paid for the fuel, he called Henry who had his nose in a very interesting clump of grass. Henry was torn between the smell he was investigating and his love for Pete but, as always, he came to his owner. They waved goodbye to Fred and Stefan and continued on their way.

Rosie and Skipper Pete were going to meet an old friend at a marina. A marina is a place where lots of boats are moored in a large lake. Some of the boats are lived on and some are just visited at weekends and for holidays. At this marina there was also a boatyard where boats were repaired. One of Pete's old friends from the navy, Sam, worked here as a mechanic fixing boat engines. Rosie had known Sam for many years and liked him very much but Henry was not so sure. Sam always smelt of oil because of his job and Henry was happier with 'country' smells.

They had one more lock to go down before they reached the marina. This stretch of the canal was right alongside a main road. This was normally a very noisy section but today there was a traffic jam with cars and lorries in a queue. All the vehicles and their drivers were looking really bored so Rosie became the centre of attention when she entered the lock. While Rosie chatted with a truck called Ellie

May, Pete climbed over the fence and talked with the driver and Henry ran round in circles, amusing a family sitting in a car. Ellie May was carrying a load of Easter eggs to a supermarket warehouse, 50,000 of them! Being a boat, Rosie didn't eat chocolate, but she could imagine the delight on children's faces when they were given the brightly wrapped eggs in a few weeks time. After a while the traffic started moving again very slowly. Pete and Henry went back to Rosie and descended the lock. Pete opened the gates for Rosie to cruise out, closed them after her and then climbed aboard for the last mile and a half to the marina.

When they arrived Skipper Pete immediately went to the workshop to find Sam. As usual he found Sam's feet before the rest of him as he was underneath the boatyard van fixing something. Sam jumped up and hugged his old friend and they started chatting straight away. Henry kept his distance and busied himself with a lamppost before heading back to Rosie. Pete and Sam had agreed to meet in a local pub when Sam finished work so Pete returned to Rosie for a wash and to give Henry his tea. When Pete left again both Henry and Rosie were dozing contentedly.

The next morning Sam arrived to do a bit of work on Rosie's engine while Skipper Pete took Henry for a nice long walk. Henry often thought that the only trouble with being a ship's dog was being surrounded by water all the time, so for him, this was heaven.

After lunch they set off back the way they had come and before long came to an interesting bit of canal which Rosie had noticed the previous day and asked Pete about. This was a section about 200 metres long where the canal was actually part of the river. The river entered on one side and then left over a weir a bit farther on. This was a shortcut for the builders of the canal but boats and their crews had to be careful in rainy weather as the water level could rise and fall quite dramatically. Rosie was just remembering what Pete had told her when she saw Fred the fuel boat again. He was clearly in difficulty with black smoke pouring from his exhaust pipe, very muddy water being churned up all around him and Stefan waving his arms like a windmill.

"This could be a job for Rescue Rosie," said our blue superhero to Skipper Pete. "Let's find out what has happened to Fred and Stefan".

After Rosie had talked to Fred and Pete had talked to Stefan it became clear that Fred had been loaded with more fuel and then got stuck on some mud washed into the canal by the heavy rain a couple of days ago. The water level had since dropped leaving Fred well and truly stuck.

"The only way we can refloat Fred", said Skipper Pete, "is to unload his cargo so he floats off but how can we do that?"

Rosie had noticed a flat boat moored by the last lock. This kind of boat is used by workmen who maintain the canal and is usually just called a flat. It doesn't have an engine or cabin and has to be towed.

Rosie told Pete her plan. She was really excited and was speaking very fast. She was going to be Rescue Rosie again. Pete had to tell her to speak more slowly so that he could understand what she was saying. They told Fred and Stefan what they were going to do and then reversed back to the lock to collect the flat. When they returned to Fred, Stefan and Pete started moving the gas and coal over to the flat. As the load got lighter Fred could feel the mud slowly loosening its grip on his hull. After a couple of hours work there was a big 'glug', some muddy bubbles and Fred was floating again and feeling a lot more comfortable. Trying to get off the mud himself had been very tiring for poor old Fred but he had been able to rest while the unloading was taking place. Now he, with Rosie towing the loaded flat boat, moved to a deeper part of the canal where Stefan and Pete moved all the coal and gas back into Fred's hold. This time, although he sank deeper in the water, he was still floating even after the very last bag of coal had been moved across.

When all the heavy lifting was done Pete and Stefan looked hot, tired and black with coal dust. They agreed that they would have a wash and then Pete would go aboard Fred and share a big bowl of goulash that Stefan had made the previous night. Goulash is a type of tasty stew that Stefan often made to remind him of his mother's cooking in his home country. Stefan even gave Henry a taste of this hearty stew, as he had been a great help getting under people's feet and generally causing chaos.

Fred told Rosie how grateful he was for all her help and as you can imagine she was very modest about her part in the rescue. Skipper Pete and Henry stayed on Fred late into the night but Rosie did not mind. She was happy, as once again she was Rescue Rosie – a friend to those in need.

Puzzle answer:
Alrewas, Trent and Mersey Canal.

Chapter 4

Rescue Rosie's Italian Job

W hen Rosie woke up she found that it was a cold winter's morning. The previous evening as she climbed the last two locks of the day on this Staffordshire canal the weather had started to get worse. Skipper Pete had tapped the old barometer that he had kept from his days in the navy. The needle swung round from Fair to Change and he knew that there was a storm brewing. Looking outside he saw the dark sky, the temperature was falling and there was a wind strengthening.

"I don't like the look of this, Rosie," he said to his old friend. "The sooner we get moored up the better."

Fifteen minutes later Rosie had eased against the canal bank and Pete had tied her up.

She hadn't slept well. It had snowed heavily, the wind had buffeted her and the canal was beginning to freeze over. When she heard Skipper Pete and

Henry moving about she knew it must be daytime again. She tried to open her eyes but all she could see was white. They were covered in snow.

"Well Rosie," said Pete as he stoked the little stove that kept the inside of the boat warm, "that was quite a night. There is at least a foot of snow out there and it has drifted in places."

"Skipper Pete, it was horrid. My eyes are covered in snow and I have a huge weight of snow on my roof. I like looking at the snow covered countryside but I can't see anything!"

"Don't worry, I'll clear all that off before we get going."

He finished work on the stove and Henry crawled back by the hearth to bask in the warmth. Pete then put on his warm clothes and went outside to clean the snow off of his boating companion.

"OK Rosie, that's you done. Let's get started and be on our way. Take it steady now. I don't think the ice is too thick but we'd better go slowly." People who don't know about canals would find this rather funny. A boat normally travels at about four miles per hour so the idea of 'going slowly' seems a bit of a joke. Rosie knew what Pete meant though, if the ice became too thick she would end up pushing large sheets in front of her or just come to a complete standstill.

She started her engine with a puff of smoke and was ready to go. Just next to the first lock there was a bridge where Rosie stopped. Pete lifted Henry off so he could have a short walk. Henry was only a small dog so if Pete had put him down in the snow he would have completely disappeared.

At the side of this lock was a round tower, which Pete explained was a lookout post for the toll keeper. In the days when canals were used for moving goods they charged boats according to what they were carrying and the weight. This money helped pay for the maintenance of the waterway.

Once through the lock Rosie kept her speed down as she cut through the ice. The thickness varied, it was thin under trees and thicker out in the open. As she glided along it made interesting noises, some of which sounded like a bullet from a gun. The countryside was very quiet and it seemed as though Rosie was the only one on the move. Then she saw a robin standing on a snow covered hedge looking for any remaining hawthorn berries and below him she could see tracks made by a fox. After a while they passed a farm with an apple orchard. The trees were now covered in snow but on the top branches she could see a thrush and a blackbird, both searching for berries and fruit. Below them a pair of white geese were digging in the snow with their beaks, trying to find the grass underneath. Rosie could hardly see them but as they lifted their heads she saw the orange of their beaks standing out from the white blanket that covered the countryside.

"You're brave being out on the water," said the male goose to Rosie, "I said to Gloria here, I said, 'I wouldn't want to be out on the water in this weather'."

"He doesn't like the ice you see," said the female. "Gerald," I said, "if you don't like the ice, don't go in the water, it's not difficult you know!"

Rosie replied, "I have a nice strong hull so it doesn't hurt too much. Why don't you swim along behind me where the ice is broken up?"

The two geese thought that this was a terrific idea, flew in to the water and started swimming about happily in Rosie's wake.

It was just so peaceful. Skipper Pete had come out of the warm cabin and was standing on the back deck admiring the view and the silence. Henry, however, was still inside. He decided that, although he had more legs and feet to grip the slippery surfaces than Pete, he was safer by the stove so this is where he stayed.

As Rosie rounded a sharp bend she saw the railway line. This was a main route and normally it was busy with brightly coloured trains dashing north and south but today even that was peaceful too. She could see in the distance the grey and red shape of a sleek train standing still. "He must be stopped at a signal," she thought but when she came round the next bend to the railway bridge she found the front of the train was stopped over the canal.

"Hello, what are you doing here? Is there a red signal?"

"There is no red signal. I 'ave no power. The cables must be broken with the snow. I 'ave been 'ere for five 'ours. My driver can't contact the signalman to tell 'im what is wrong because the communication

system does not work. The mobile telephones do not work 'ere either.

"My name is Leonardo Pendolino, I am from Turino in Italy. I am so un'appy. I should be speeding along in the Italian sunshine not standing 'ere in the snow. Every day I go between London and Manchester. That is no way to treat someone as beautiful as me.

"My batteries are almost dead, I 'ave been 'ere so long. What will 'appen to me?"

"Don't worry," said our snow-covered superhero. "My name is Rosie, Rescue Rosie. Skipper Pete and I will help you."

Pete realised that swift action was needed as the snow had started again. With difficulty he climbed up the embankment to speak to the driver. It turned out that the situation was more serious than Leonardo had said. There was a sick lady on the train who needed to be kept warm and taken to hospital urgently. The rest of the passengers and train crew were getting very cold and also needed rescuing. One of the train company's employees had struggled along the track to raise the alarm but found his path blocked by a snowdrift in a cutting. He had fought his way through and eventually been able to tell the controllers what had happened, but any rescue efforts were being hampered by the weather. They couldn't use the rescue helicopter or get another train to help.

Skipper Pete knew that the sick lady was the top priority so with the help of three passengers

and train crew he used the train's stretcher to carry the patient down the embankment to where Rosie was waiting. A doctor who had been on the train had said that he thought that the patient had appendicitis so he struggled through the snow as well and helped settle the distressed lady in front of the stove in Rosie's cabin. The ten children from the train were also brought down the embankment by their parents and settled on Rosie. It was very cramped in the cabin but no one complained. They were so grateful to be somewhere warm.

Pete's plan was to take this first load of passengers about half a mile along the canal to a place where there was a pub, which was close to a main road. Everyone could be kept comfortable there while Rosie went back for the next group of passengers.

The wind was getting stronger and the temperature dropping further as the snow still came down. Rosie knew that the first trip would be the most difficult as she cut her way through the ice. Later journeys would be in the channel she had made and would be faster.

She carefully edged her precious cargo away from the bank and along the canal. The sound of the ice breaking in front of her sounded more alarming now as it was getting thicker. She found herself pushing great sheets of ice out of the way and came to a complete stop a couple of times. When this happened she would have to reverse and then ram the blockage.

After half an hour they had reached the pub.

Skipper Pete went in to speak to the landlord and get things organised. Fortunately the road near the pub was being kept open with snowploughs and gritters so the ambulance requested by the landlord would be able to get through. Rosie's passengers where taken into the pub where they were given hot drinks and some food. Henry stayed at the pub to amuse the children while they waited for a bus to come and complete their rescue. The patient was settled in a bedroom and was very grateful to be still while she waited for the ambulance.

Rosie knew that she had plenty more work to do so she and Pete turned round and headed back to the train to rescue the next group of passengers.

When she got back to Leonardo he said, "Bravo Rosie, you 'ave done well. My passengers are so 'appy that you will rescue them."

She did this trip five more times until all the passengers and crew had been transported to the pub. As she started her last trip she said to Leonardo, "Don't worry my friend, all your passengers are safe now and soon another train will come and rescue you." Leonardo couldn't reply as his batteries were getting very low. By the time she got back with the last group it had got dark but the snow had stopped. Pete escorted the passengers to the pub and went back to his old companion and made sure she was securely tied up for the night.

"Well Rosie," he said as he entered her warm but untidy cabin," that was quite a rescue. You did good old girl. That was one hundred and twenty four people you helped today. You have really earned your name today, Rescue Rosie."

Rosie was very tired but ever so proud of herself. She knew she couldn't do any of it without Pete's help but she was the one cutting through the ice, she was the one protecting her passengers in her cabin.

Pete cleaned up the cabin and put more coal on the stove. All those people make quite a mess he thought to himself. "Hang on a minute. Where's Henry?".

Just then there was a knock on the door and there was the pub landlord with Henry under one arm and a pot of beef stew in his hand. "I thought you might appreciate this," he laughed as he put the little dog down and handed over the stew. "You must all be exhausted."

Skipper Pete thanked him and accepted the hot meal. He had been so busy that he had forgotten how hungry he was.

The next morning the thaw had started and Rosie and Pete decided to stay put so they could watch the recovery operation on the train. The ice was disappearing from the canal and diesel trains were beginning to reappear on the railway line pulling special wagons to help the engineers reconnect the electricity supply.

Rosie was feeling a bit sore round her waterline. Pete had a look to see if he could tell why and found that the ice had scraped all the paint off her hull. When he told Rosie what the problem was she knew that she would have to go into a dry dock and get repainted but at least that wasn't as bad as being picked up by a crane. That was very undignified!

Henry could now go outside as the snow was being cleared away. He would run around the pub garden and then return to Rosie. On one trip he came back with a smiley man with a beard named Richard who said that he owned the train that Rosie rescued the previous day and that he wanted to meet this courageous boat and her crew. He was ever so nice and friendly and said he wanted to pay for the repainting of her hull as a way of saying thank you.

"We'll have you looking like new again," he said.

"It will take more than a coat of paint", thought Pete, "but I love her".

Puzzle answer:
Gailey Wharf, Staffs and Worcester Canal

Chapter 5

Rescue Rosie Meets a VIP

Rescue Rosie, Skipper Pete and Henry had spent the night moored at the wharf of a small Cheshire town. It was early summer and all the canalside trees were in full leaf casting big areas of shade over the water. Rosie's face was in shade but she could feel the warmth of the morning sun on her cabin.

Pete had been out to one of the nearby pubs last night and was having a lay in. Henry, on the other hand, was up bright and early as usual. The floor of Rosie's cabin was made of wooden floorboards running long ways and Skipper Pete had put down exotic rugs that he had brought from around the world during his days in the navy. Pete liked to think of them as exotic but in reality they were getting a bit threadbare from life on the boat. Henry loved nothing more than to run the length of the boat and then slide on one of the rugs. He didn't always get it right and sometimes would find himself sliding on the wooden floor with his legs going all over the place.

On this particular morning Pete was just waking up after a very sound sleep when he heard the 'click, click' of Henry's claws on the floor as he came bounding down the boat. Just at the right time he jumped on to a rug, slid a metre and then leapt on to Pete's bed. Pete hadn't quite expected this and let out a deep groan. He realised that there would be no peace until his little friend had been fed and so got out of bed to prepare for the day.

After breakfast he sat in his favourite armchair drinking a second mug of coffee and laughed with Rosie about what they had seen yesterday. They had been going up a couple of locks when Pete had seen a sign that was still making him laugh. It said, "Secret nuclear bunker 200 yards" and then underneath it said "Temporary sign". The sign was very overgrown with weeds so Pete doubted it was temporary and certainly doubted that the bunker was secret. He had asked in the pub about it and found out a little more. It had been originally built in the 1950s as part of a secret radar network and rebuilt in the 1980s as a vast underground bunker in case there was a war. Hundreds of people could have lived down there.

It was now time to think about today's boating. They had another twelve locks to do in this flight and then two more flights of five each. Twenty-two in total but, as these were narrow locks with only room for one boat, they did not take long.

Just before they set of, Skipper Pete went into the village to buy some fresh food at the local shop and when Rosie saw him walking back along the towpath with his provisions she started her engine with a little puff of smoke.

"Are you in a hurry to get off then Rosie?" laughed Pete.

"Yes, I am a bit," replied Rosie. "There is a column of midges dancing in front of my eyes and they are very irritating."

"OK, right you are. I'll untie you and go and empty the lock. You set off when you are ready."

Skipper Pete put his food on board, undid the ropes and strolled off in the direction of the lock. Rosie eased away from the bank and left the midges behind.

They were soon at the top lock where they found a beautiful lock cottage. In the old days this would have been the home of the lock keeper responsible for the flight of locks. Since the carrying of cargo stopped many of these lovely places had been sold to make idyllic homes. The owner of this one was very enterprising and had a little canalside shop where she was selling home baked bread and cream teas. Pete loved Cornish clotted cream so he treated himself to a little paper carrier bag which contained two freshly made scones, butter, raspberry jam and the all important cream.

Fifteen minutes later they were at the bottom of the next flight of locks, only five this time and in a lovely rural setting. They were through these in no time at all and soon heading for one of the few towns on the canal. In nearly fifty miles it goes through only a handful of towns and one of them was now on the horizon. All of a sudden the peace was broken by the sound of a helicopter approaching from the west.

Skipper Pete did not know much about helicopters but he recognised it as one of the yellow ones used by the Royal Air Force for rescue missions. It was heading directly for the town and then prepared to land. As its engines stopped Pete and Rosie could hear someone speaking over a loud speaker but they were too far away to hear what was going on.

At the next set of locks, the last for the day, Pete chatted with a family out walking with their dogs and they told him that there was a charity event at the local football club and the helicopter was on show for all the visitors to look at.

They were through the locks in under an hour and had another two miles to go before they moored up for the night.

Pete decided that he just fancied his scone and cream so Rosie moved over to the side of the canal and Pete tied her up. As he was disappearing into the cabin to put the kettle on a group of around thirty schoolboys ran past on the towpath. They were obviously on a cross-country run, something that Pete had hated when he was at school a long time ago.

While Pete sat and ate his afternoon tea, Rosie was thinking how much she enjoyed this canal with its well-maintained locks and clean water. There was plenty of wildlife to see and talk to as she cruised along and it was all very peaceful.

She was rudely woken from her daydreaming by the sound of the helicopter's engines starting again and to their surprise it seemed to be heading for the canal.

"I wonder what's up," said Pete. "I'll get my radio and see if I can listen in".

He had the type of radio that was used at sea and by the rescue services. He didn't often need it these days but there are a few waterways where they are still necessary. He pressed the 'Scan' button so that it would search for the frequency the helicopter was using. When he found it the situation became clear. One of the runners had badly injured his ankle on a stretch of the towpath where the canal ran through a deep, narrow cutting. One of his fellow runners had reported it at a checkpoint so that he could be rescued. There was no road access so the helicopter had been called to winch the injured boy to safety and take him to a waiting ambulance.

"This is exciting Rosie," said Pete as he told her what was happening. "It looks like we missed out on this rescue. It would be difficult for you to compete with a helicopter."

Rosie was rather disappointed by this but kept on asking Pete what was happening. He kept on listening to the radio and Rosie could tell he was getting a bit anxious. It seemed that the helicopter crew had found where the injured boy was lying but could not get to him because of the dense tree cover.

They were used to working out in the open on the coast or out at sea.

Pete pressed the 'Transmit' button on the radio and started talking to the pilot. It was agreed that Rosie and Pete would go into the cutting and collect the boy and take him to the other end where an ambulance was waiting. Before they set off the helicopter would come back to them and drop off a crew member with a stretcher.

When Pete told Rosie what was going to happen, she thought to herself "Rosie to the rescue once more!" Her excitement didn't last long as the helicopter came overhead ready to winch down the stretcher and crewman. Rosie had never been underneath a helicopter before and the noise was deafening. Henry went and hid in his little kennel with his head under his bedding. The wind from the rotor blades was really alarming both for Rosie and for a flotilla of ducks that had been minding their own business in some reeds nearby. She was bouncing about in the water and soon started feeling seasick.

As soon as the stretcher and crewman had been lowered on the winch the helicopter flew off to wait with the ambulance at the other end of the cutting. Now everything was quiet and normal again Rosie felt better and ready to get on with the rescue.

She cruised into the cutting and after five minutes they could see the injured boy lying at the side of the towpath. It was really dark and gloomy in the cutting but they could see him due to his white running gear. At least it was white when he started but most of it was covered in mud by now. The towpath was very muddy and must have been terribly slippery. When they got alongside the boy, Pete and the helicopter crewman put the boy on the stretcher and lifted him on to Rosie's roof. The boy was clearly in a lot of pain so Rosie was very careful as she cruised along the rest of the cutting to where the ambulance and helicopter were waiting.

When they got there they were surprised to see so many people. When the crowd saw Rosie coming into view everyone cheered and clapped. The helicopter had landed right by the side of the canal and the ambulance, a police car and the crowd of onlookers were all waiting in the pub car park. A space had been made for Rosie on the mooring outside the pub and as soon as she was alongside the ambulance men lifted the injured boy from the roof and started tending to his injury.

Both Skipper Pete and Rosie were surprised by the fuss being made until the helicopter pilot climbed out of his cockpit and came over to them. It wasn't until he took off his flying helmet that they realised that it was none other than Prince William, the Duke of Cambridge. He smiled broadly and came over to speak to Pete and thank him for his help in the rescue. Pete went bright red with embarrassment and couldn't find the right words at first but he managed to remember to bow. The prince quickly put him at ease and Pete relaxed again.

Rosie had never met royalty before although she had spent quite a bit of time moored outside

Prince Alberts, Kings Arms and Queen Victorias. As Pete got over the shock and started talking with the prince, Rosie heard a voice from behind her. It was the helicopter. "I'm sorry if a scared you earlier when I winched the stretcher down. I'm afraid I don't do quiet!"

"Oh no, I wasn't scared," said Rosie. "As Rescue Rosie I am ready for anything." They both laughed, but both knew the truth.

When the ambulance had departed with its patient, the helicopter had returned to its base and the crowd dispersed, it was just Rosie, Skipper Pete and Henry again.

"You did well there, Rosie," said Pete to his old friend. "This has been quite an experience. It is not every day that you meet a VIP"

"What's a VIP?"

"Very Important Pilot."

Puzzle answer:
Audlem – Cheswardine, Shropshire Union Canal

Chapter 6

Rosie's Christmas Rescue

I t was Christmas Eve and Rescue Rosie was cruising along an urban canal in the south of England. It was a greyish sort of day, not warm and not cold. The weatherman had said that it was unlikely to be a white Christmas but Rosie still loved this time of year. She normally preferred being in the countryside to being in towns but at Christmas it was different. Everywhere looked so pretty with coloured lights hanging from lampposts and decorated Christmas trees in public gardens and town centres. Then there were the streets of houses where you would find one house trying to outdo all their neighbours with their decorations, sometimes tasteful but always bright.

Rosie loved to see the mountains of presents and usually received at least one gift of her own. Last year it was a can of engine oil of her favourite brand!

Rosie herself was decorated this year. Normally Skipper Pete would put a little tree with lights and decorations up in her cabin but this year he had really gone to town. He had even bought Henry a flashing collar, which he was now wearing.

The reason for this change was that Rosie, Pete and Henry were having Pete's nephew and niece to stay over Christmas. Their parents both worked in a local hospital and it was their turn to work over Christmas so they asked the twins, Adam and Susie, whether they would like to spend Christmas on the canal. Without a moment's hesitation they had said, 'Yes' and it was all arranged. A sleepover is always exciting for an eight year old, but one on a boat and at Christmas, it was a 'no brainer' as Adam now said at every opportunity. He had heard his father say it, didn't know what it meant, but liked the sound of it.

The plan was that Adam and Susie and their parents would meet up with Skipper Pete in the evening and all go to a Christmas pantomime together before the unlucky doctors went off to work.

The stretch of canal that Rosie was on was twenty-seven miles long with no locks so Pete had taken the opportunity to walk along the towpath with Henry while Rosie cruised along beside them. This part of the canal system was always crowded. There were lots of boats moored up and a boat about half a mile in front of them going in the same direction. It was easy to tell the houseboats as they were gaily decorated with flashing fairy lights and inflatable reindeers and Santas.

Rosie had to slow down to pass some moored boats so Skipper Pete was a little way ahead of her.

She saw him stop and lean over some railings looking at something below him. When she caught up with him she realised he had stopped on an aqueduct over a main road and was looking at the traffic. An aqueduct is a bridge that carries a canal over a road, river or railway. When they were first built, over two hundred years ago, people where amazed to see boats 'flying' above them. This particular aqueduct carried the canal over a six-lane road full of stationary traffic. Rosie could hear two trucks talking below but she couldn't see them as they were ten metres below her.

"This road gets worse each year," said the delivery truck whose name was Bernie. "I've promised to deliver this sofa by Christmas and I'm running out of time. Where are you heading for? I didn't catch your name."

"I am Hans," said the giant articulated lorry. "I have made my last delivery of washing machines to a warehouse ready for the sales and I'm now heading back to Germany for Christmas. I am supposed to be on the ferry in Dover in two hours but I don't think I will make it. My driver will be so sad not to be with his family on Christmas morning."

"I know what you mean Hans, I have only got a few miles to go and then return to the depot so…. Hang on a minute, we're moving. See you later Hans and Merry Christmas."

"Good news. Merry Christmas to you Bernie. Fröhliche Weihnachten as we say in Germany and good luck."

Rosie could hear the traffic moving a few metres

and was a bit sad as she too moved on leaving the poor stranded drivers behind.

"There are some people, old girl, that even you cannot rescue," said Pete as he chuckled to himself. "I'll climb aboard now Rosie, Henry and I have walked far enough." Rosie pulled in to the canal bank and when her crew was safely aboard carried on her way.

Skipper Pete was particularly looking forward to seeing the twins and especially the pantomime. It was being put on by a travelling theatre group which normally spent the summer cruising the canals and performing in pubs and village halls. This year they were celebrating their fiftieth anniversary and putting on their first ever pantomime, performing at a different location every night and tonight was going to be the last show. Pete knew that all children loved a Christmas panto and he loved seeing the wonder on their faces as the story unfolded.

After another hour they reached a canal junction. It was a big triangular expanse of water with an island in the middle. There were loads of visitors looking at the canal boats and queuing for the trip boat called Jason. Jason had been working here for many years and took his passengers for a cruise of about four miles so they could see a different side to this big city. Away from the traffic it was possible to see a large variety of wildlife and on the island there were a pair of swans with their teenage children. The cygnets were still covered in grey feathers but in a few weeks would start turning white like their parents.

After a brief stop to talk to Jason, Rosie continued

on her way towards a short tunnel. There were boats moored on both sides of the canal, all of them brightly decorated. It was a lovely atmosphere.

As she was about to enter the tunnel she noticed that she couldn't see the normal disk of white light that you see looking straight through a canal tunnel.

"That must mean that there is a boat already in the tunnel," thought Rosie to herself. "It doesn't matter because this tunnel is wide enough for two boats to pass. There was a boat in front of me so it might be them just going slowly."

She switched on her headlight and plunged into the tunnel. After five minutes she could see the outline of the other boat not moving. She slowed down even more as she approached the stationary boat. Pete had realised that something was up and had come to the front of Rosie to see what the problem was for himself. He called out to the crew of the boat who had seen Rosie approaching. It was the boat belonging to the theatre group and it had broken down. They had been having trouble with the engine for a few miles but now it had stopped and would not restart.

The actors on board were all very anxious as they knew they had to get to the venue for tonight's show because they didn't want to let down all those families who had bought tickets and made the journey to see them.

"Don't worry," said Pete, "this is Rescue Rosie and she will get you there safely".

Rosie squeezed past the broken down boat who

was called Daphne. Pete tied a rope from Daphne's front to Rosie's back and she started towing the rather downcast boat out of the dark. After they were out of the tunnel the two boats started chatting together. Daphne was an old working boat, around 120 years old, who used to carry cargo but had now been with the theatre group for 50 years.

She loved her new life. She normally rested during the winter but this year had been a special celebration and she was finding it hard on her old engine. This was the last few miles before she could relax and she was really disappointed to have let everyone down. Rosie told her not to worry as they were going to the show anyway and helping out just made the day more exciting.

They were soon approaching a zoo that had animal enclosures on both sides of the canal. On one side was a giant aviary filled with a huge variety of exotic birds. Rosie did not recognise any of them and, to be honest, the birds seemed more interested in flying from tree to tree and squabbling than remarking on the rare sight of one boat towing another. On the other side of the canal was the African enclosure. The giraffes had a wonderful view of the canal and the city all around them. Two adults of the herd, Berko and his mate Anaya, were particularly interested.

"You don't see that everyday," said Berko.

"No you don't, " replied Anaya. "What is it?"

"It can't be a snake. It's too long for a snake. It could be a boat but it's a bit long for that as well."

"I'm Rescue Rosie", exclaimed our heroine. "I've rescued poor Daphne here and we are going to see a pantomime this evening."

"Oh I see," said Berko, not seeing at all. "Now you mention it, it's obvious". He then whispered to Anaya. "I haven't a clue what they are talking about. A panto thingy? Isn't that a large black cat that lives in the trees?"

"No dear, that's a panther," replied Anaya. "A panto is something that humans do and people shout, 'He's behind you' and then everyone falls about laughing".

"I'll never understand humans."

Just as Rosie was beginning to realise that this conversation was not going to get anywhere soon, she saw a magical thing. Two reindeer were pulling a sleigh stacked with presents and being driven by none other than Father Christmas himself. They had come over the bridge across the canal and had stopped next to a group of children. He was too busy handing out presents to notice Rosie. This was the first time that she had ever seen Santa and she was very impressed.

After another half an hour they came to the first of four locks that took the canal down about ten metres. Skipper Pete and Daphne's crew put the boats side by side, which meant that they could talk more easily. Daphne started telling Rosie about their destination.

The pantomime was being put on in a canal museum in an old warehouse built over an ice pit. In the old days, before electricity, fridges and freezers, an Italian man started to import ice from

Norway so that he could make ice cream. The ice was transported to the docks in big ships and then moved to the ice pit on the canal. The ice was then sold to food manufacturers and rich families who often had icehouses in a particularly cold part of their large gardens. Rosie didn't like the idea of transporting ice and Daphne admitted that she had never done it but had met very old boats that had. They had said that it used to freeze their rivets!

It was beginning to get dark as Rosie and Daphne arrived at the museum. There were crowds of people waiting for the doors to open including Adam and Susie and their parents. They all waved when they saw Rosie approaching. There was only room for one boat next to the museum so Rosie helped Daphne moor up there and then went to tie up over the other side of the canal. All the actors were relieved to have made it to the last venue of their tour and Daphne was glad that she could now have a well earned rest.

The twins rushed across the footbridge to say hallo to their Uncle Pete. He changed into his only set of smart clothes and then went to enjoy the pantomime leaving Rosie to think about today's adventure. Henry was asleep in front of the stove and she was happy.

Rosie heard all the cheering and laughter from the performance and before long Pete and the children came back on board chattering excitedly. He put Adam and Susie to bed in the two bunks and then settled next to Henry by the stove with a drink.

"Well done Rosie," he said. "You saved the day

yet again and helped make it a happy Christmas for a lot of families and a group of lovely actors. Happy Christmas to you too."

The next morning when Rosie woke up she could hardly believe it. It was actually snowing. It was going to be a white Christmas after all. The twins were up early which woke Pete and Henry and soon her cabin was a hive of activity. The children were really excited, as there was now a heap of presents under the tree including ones addressed to Rosie and Henry. Pete was puzzled though, he had put a mince pie and a glass of sherry out for Santa and this morning there was a bite missing from the pie and the glass was now half empty. This really was turning out to be a magical Christmas.

Puzzle answer:
Grand Union and Regents Canals